Maths Sticker Work
Maths Puzzles

Wendy Clemson and David Clemson

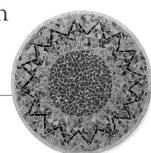

Note to parents

This book is part of a programme of workbook titles that are designed to support school-work and make learning fun. Each page covers a different mathematical topic and provides example exercises. Guide your child through the examples before he or she tries the practice exercises.

Many of the questions and puzzles in **Maths Puzzles** are answered with stickers, which are found on the middle two pages of the book. Your child will need plenty of scrap paper on which to write down the calculations featured on each page before he or she can start to work out the answers. All answers are provided on page 16.

How to use this book:

 The star sign means there is a sticker to put here on the page.

 Wherever your child needs to fill in an answer, there is a blue box like this one to write in.

 The calculator picture appears whenever a calculator is needed to solve a puzzle.

 In the top left-hand corner of each page there is a space for a "reward" sticker. Your child can add it when he or she has completed the puzzles.

DORLING KINDERSLEY

LONDON • NEW YORK • MUNICH • MELBOURNE • DELHI

Fun and games

Test out your skills in addition, subtraction, multiplication, and division by completing these games and puzzles.

Badminton colours

These shuttlecocks all have numbers on them. If the number can be exactly divided by 2, colour the cork red. If the number can be exactly divided by 5, colour the band blue. If the number can be exactly divided by 10, colour the feathers orange.

Band   Feathers

Cork

16
76
450
30
108
80
102
100
31
50
700
35
365
500
60

Batty additions

Add together the numbers on the table tennis balls to make the numbers on the bats. Use each number once only. Write your answers in the boxes below.

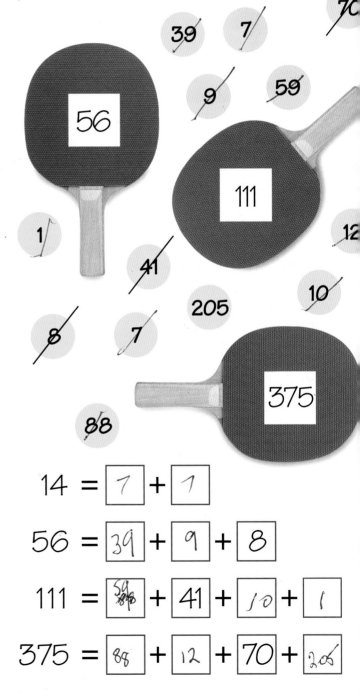

14

39 7 76

9 59

56

111

1

41

12

8 7

205

10

375

88

$$14 = \boxed{7} + \boxed{7}$$

$$56 = \boxed{39} + \boxed{9} + \boxed{8}$$

$$111 = \boxed{59} + \boxed{41} + \boxed{10} + \boxed{1}$$

$$375 = \boxed{88} + \boxed{12} + \boxed{70} + \boxed{205}$$

got n o ticks

Singles and doubles

A sports club has facilities for playing tennis, badminton, and table tennis. A game of singles is played by 2 people, and a game of doubles is played by 4 people. Use the key below to answer the questions.

Key	
Sport	Facilities
Tennis	7 courts
Badminton	8 courts
Table tennis	6 tables

How many people can play singles tennis?

How many people can play singles badminton?

How many people can play doubles table tennis?

How many people can play doubles tennis?

Net numbers

Solve the clues and fill in the answers on the net.

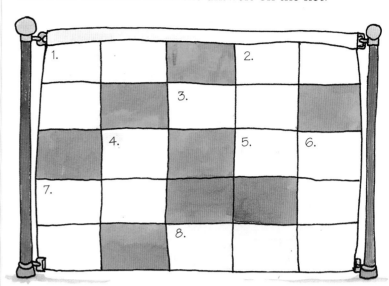

Across
1. 46 − 30 =
2. 38 − 5 =
3. 100 − 35 =
5. 28 − 7 =
7. 59 − 41 =
8. 168 − 12 =

Down
1. 23 − 4 =
2. 460 − 108 =
4. 72 − 14 =
6. 203 − 7 =
7. 17 − 3 =

Court calculations

Follow the calculation trail around the court. The answer is smaller than the number you start with – but there are some tough calculations on the way.

Start | 320 ÷ 16 ☆ − 10 ☆ + (3 x 8)

− 17

− 9

x (12 x 5)

Finish

÷ 3

− 3 ☆ ÷ 11 ☆ − 282 ☆

Number patterns

Find out more about how numbers relate to each other and form patterns. These camping puzzles include exercises on odd, even, prime, square, and consecutive numbers.

Square numbers

Square numbers are made by multiplying a number by itself.

$1 \times 1 = 1$
1 is a square number.

$2 \times 2 = 4$
4 is a square number.

$3 \times 3 = 9$
9 is a square number.

Footprints in the sand

Work out the first 12 square numbers and fill them in on the footprint trail.

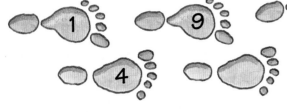

Camp fire

All whole numbers are either odd or even.
1 is the first odd number, 2 is the first even number. Alternate numbers starting at 1 are odd. Alternate numbers starting at 2 are even. You can divide all even numbers by 2.

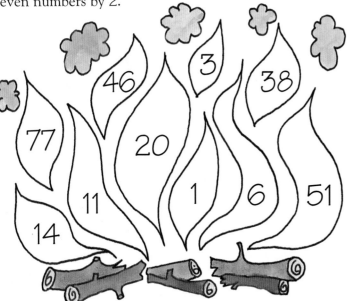

Look at the numbers on the flames. Colour the odd numbers red and the even numbers yellow.

Bear tracks

Find sticker answers to the following calculations and discover a link between odd numbers and square numbers.

Add the first 2 odd numbers

$1 + 3 =$

Add the first 3 odd numbers

$1 + 3 + 5 =$

Add the first 4 odd numbers

$1 + 3 + 5 + 7 =$

Add the first 5 odd numbers

$1 + 3 + 5 + 7 + 9 =$

Do you think this pattern will continue?
Test it out on your calculator.
Try as many numbers as you like.

Consecutive numbers

Numbers that follow one another are called consecutive. If 2 consecutive numbers are added together a number pattern occurs. Discover the number pattern by adding together the consecutive numbers on the sleeping bag opposite.

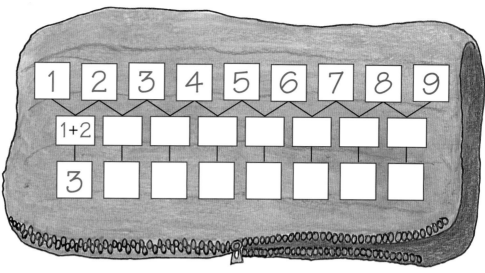

| 1 | 2 | 3 | 4 | 5 | 6 | 7 | 8 | 9 |

| 1+2 | | | | | | | |

| 3 | | | | | | | |

What is the name for the numbers in the pattern? _____

Torch light

A prime number can only be divided exactly by itself and 1. The first prime number is 2, the next prime number is 3.

Work out the next 6 prime numbers, then fill in the torch with the correct sticker answers.

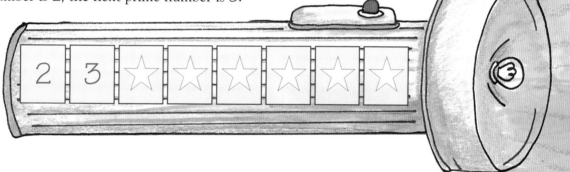

| 2 | 3 | ☆ | ☆ | ☆ | ☆ | ☆ | ☆ |

Prime number trail

Each of the tents below has a number. Draw a line to join up the prime numbers from the smallest to the biggest numbers.

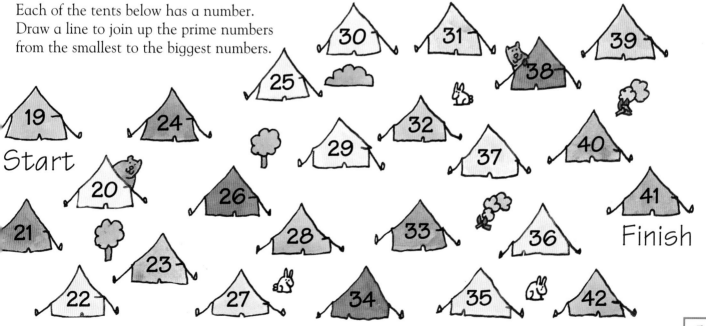

19 Start
24
25
30
31
39
38
20
29
32
37
40
21
26
33
36
41 Finish
23
28
35
42
22
27
34

2-D and 3-D shapes

Two-dimensional and three-dimensional shapes are all around us. These puzzles and exercises will help you to identify and describe them.

Length, breadth, and depth

Flat shapes are two-dimensional or 2-D. They have length and breadth, but no depth.

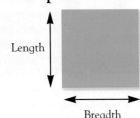

Length

Breadth

Solid shapes are three-dimensional or 3-D. Like this box, they have length, breadth, and depth.

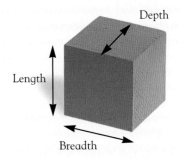

Depth

Length

Breadth

2-D descriptions

Draw lines to match the 2-D shapes below with their correct descriptions and names.

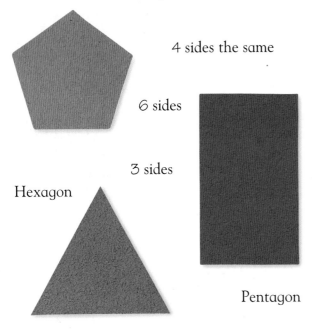

4 sides the same

6 sides

3 sides

Hexagon

Pentagon

Triangle

5 sides

Rectangle

Square

2 pairs of sides the same

Symmetry

Some shapes show one line of symmetry. They have matching halves. If you put a mirror along the line of symmetry the reflection completes the shape.

Line of symmetry

2-D symmetry

Look at these shapes and draw in the line of symmetry.

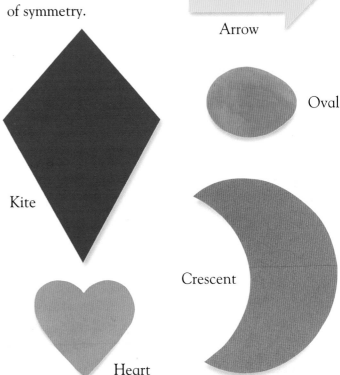

Arrow

Oval

Kite

Crescent

Heart

Faces, corners, and edges

3-D shapes have faces (the flat parts of the shape), corners, and edges. Count up the number of faces, corners, and edges for the following 3-D shapes.

	Faces	Corners	Edges
	☆	☆	☆
	☆	☆	☆
	☆	☆	☆
	☆	☆	☆

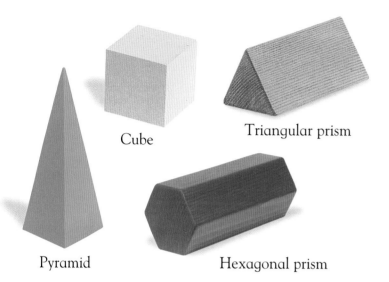

Cube

Triangular prism

Pyramid

Hexagonal prism

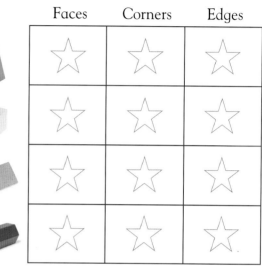

Polyhedra

A solid shape that has only flat (or plane) faces is called a polyhedron. How many polyhedra are there here?

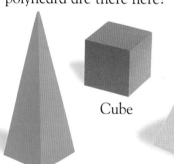

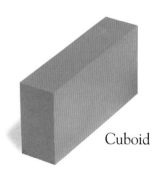

Pyramid

Cube

Prism

Cone

Cylinder

Cuboid

Number of polyhedra

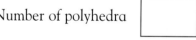

A polyhedron that has faces and corners that all match is called 'regular'. Colour the regular polyhedra red.

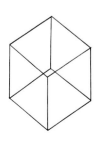

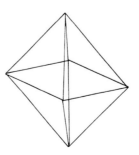

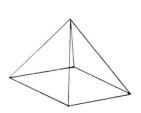

Cube

Tetrahedron

Octahedron

Pyramid

7

Averages

The information about timing and phone calls here will help you understand what is meant by 'average'. There are 3 different averages – mean, median, or mode.

Phoning friends

A list showing how long our phone calls are might look like this:

Friend	Time of call
John	6 minutes
Susan	8 minutes
Saheed	4 minutes
Rena	3 minutes
Kathy	2 minutes
Saheed	8 minutes
Jane	5 minutes
Martin	5 minutes
Susan	12 minutes
John	16 minutes
Martin	8 minutes

Mean

To find the mean length of call, add all the call times together then divide them by the total number of calls.

$$77 \div 11 = 7 \text{ minutes}$$

Total call time — Number of calls — Mean length of call

Mode

The mode is the time that appears most often. 8 minutes appears most often.

The mode is 8 minutes

Median

To find the median we first need to put the calls in order. Start with the shortest call and finish with the longest call.

2 3 4 5 5 ⑥ 8 8 8 12 16

The median is the middle number.

The median is 6 minutes

Busy line

Now work out the mean, mode, and median length of the phone calls below. Find the correct sticker answers.

Call	Time of call	Mean call time
Call 1	4 minutes	☆
Call 2	6 minutes	
Call 3	14 minutes	
Call 4	4 minutes	Mode call time
Call 5	9 minutes	
Call 6	5 minutes	☆
Call 7	4 minutes	Median call time
Call 8	5 minutes	
Call 9	3 minutes	☆

TV competition

Hundreds of people phone in to enter a TV competition. There are 7 operators to answer the calls. Work out the average number of calls each operator receives. Find the mean, mode, and median.

Operator	1	2	3	4	5	6	7
Number of calls	100	1600	700	600	500	200	500

Mean number of calls

Mode number of calls

Median number of calls

2/3 Fun and games
Court calculations

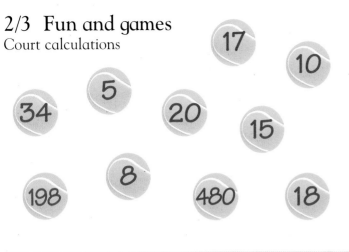

4/5 Number patterns
Bear tracks

Torch light

| 11 | 19 | 7 | 5 | 17 | 13 |

6/7 2-D and 3-D Shapes
Faces, corners, and edges

5	5	5	6
6	8	8	8
9	12	12	18

8 Averages
Busy line

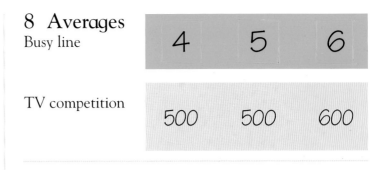

TV competition

| 500 | 500 | 600 |

9 Timing

10/11 Charts and graphs
Saddle chart

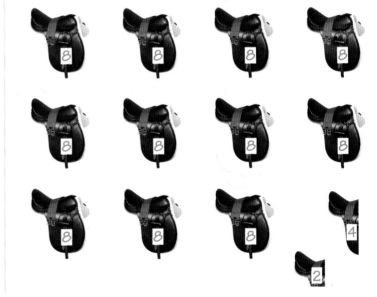

Reward stickers
When a page is completed
and the answers checked,
reward yourself with the
right sticker.

12/13 Fractions

Mosaic circles

$$\frac{1}{8} \quad \frac{1}{2} \quad \frac{1}{12} \quad \frac{1}{6} \quad \frac{1}{5} \quad \frac{1}{4}$$

Panel colours

$$\frac{1}{9} \quad \frac{4}{9} \quad \frac{1}{9} \quad \frac{3}{9}$$

Fraction subtraction

$$\frac{2}{4} \quad \frac{1}{3} \quad \frac{3}{6} \quad \frac{4}{10}$$

14/15 Lions and tigers

Answer card

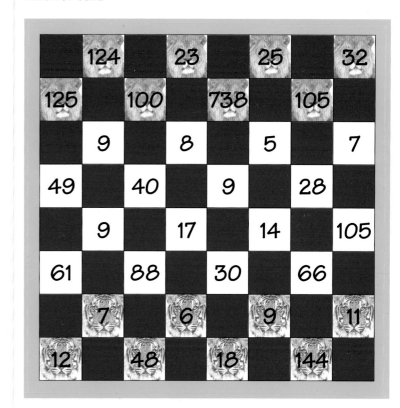

Lion and tiger counters

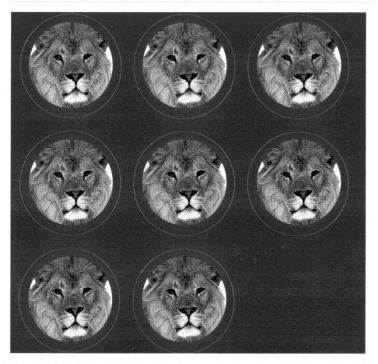

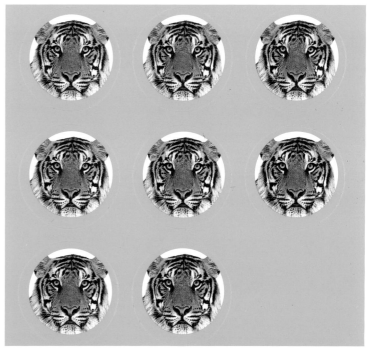

Timing

Below are 3 great days out, all mixed up. Unjumble the days out by working out the timing of the activities. Then make a record of each day using the stickers. Which day out would you choose?

Here are some clues to help you

- Each day out has 4 activities plus the journey home.
- Each day out finishes at home at 6 o'clock.
- Use the same means of transport for the outward journey and the journey home.
- Leave a 5-minute gap between each activity.
- Start each day out with a transport symbol.
- Start times and the length of each activity are given under each activity symbol.

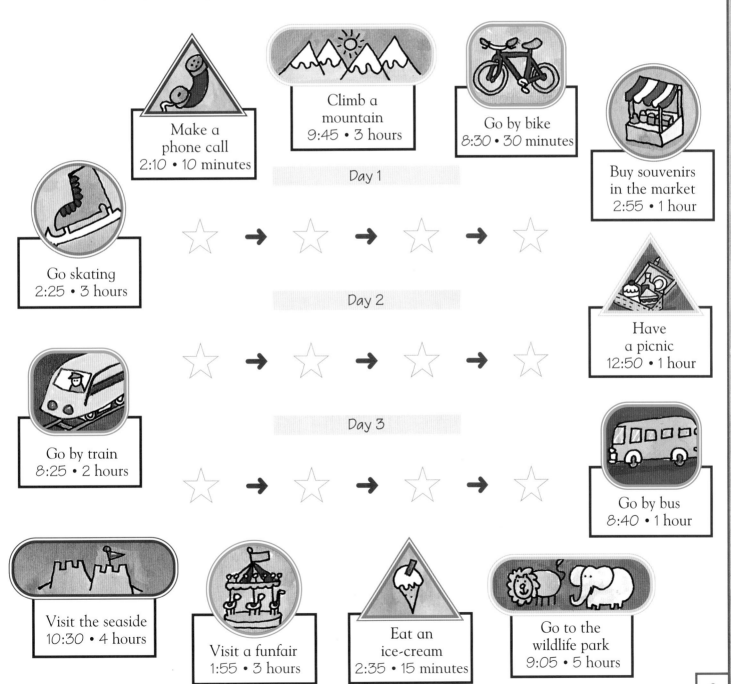

Make a phone call
2:10 • 10 minutes

Climb a mountain
9:45 • 3 hours

Go by bike
8:30 • 30 minutes

Buy souvenirs in the market
2:55 • 1 hour

Day 1

☆ → ☆ → ☆ → ☆

Go skating
2:25 • 3 hours

Day 2

☆ → ☆ → ☆ → ☆

Have a picnic
12:50 • 1 hour

Go by train
8:25 • 2 hours

Day 3

☆ → ☆ → ☆ → ☆

Go by bus
8:40 • 1 hour

Visit the seaside
10:30 • 4 hours

Visit a funfair
1:55 • 3 hours

Eat an ice-cream
2:35 • 15 minutes

Go to the wildlife park
9:05 • 5 hours

9

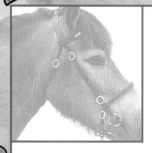

Charts and graphs

Charts and graphs show mathematical information clearly. Use the riding school information to practise creating and reading different types of charts and graphs.

Pony rides

This tally chart shows the number of times the riding school ponies were chosen by young riders in one month. Fill in the totals and answer the questions.

Horse	Tally	Total
Amber	＼＼＼＼ ＼＼＼＼ ＼＼＼＼ ＼＼＼＼	20
Lucy	＼＼＼＼ ＼＼＼＼ ＼＼＼＼ ‖‖	
Monty	＼＼＼＼ ＼＼＼＼ ＼＼＼＼ ＼＼＼＼ ＼＼＼＼ ＼＼＼＼ ‖	
Star	＼＼＼＼ ＼＼＼＼ ＼＼＼＼ ＼＼＼＼ ‖‖‖‖	

Which pony had the most rides during the month?

_____

Which pony had fewer than 20 rides in the month?

_____

How many rides were there in total?

[   ]

Saddle chart

Create a chart showing how many rides each pony had in the month. Use the information in the tally chart above and the saddle stickers below.

1 saddle represents 8 rides.

$\frac{1}{2}$ saddle represents 4 rides.

$\frac{1}{4}$ saddle represents 2 rides.

Amber

☆ ☆ ☆

Lucy

☆ ☆ ☆

Monty

☆ ☆ ☆ ☆

Star

☆ ☆ ☆

Monty wins

The rosettes on this chart show the number of times Monty has come first, second, and third in pony competitions. Study the chart and answer the questions.

1st									
2nd									
3rd									

How many rosettes has Monty won in total?

How many times has Monty come first?

What is the difference between the number of rosettes for second place and the number for third place?

Block graph

Colour in the correct number of blocks in each coloumn to show Monty's competition results.

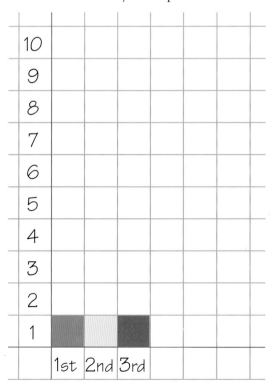

10						
9						
8						
7						
6						
5						
4						
3						
2						
1						
	1st	2nd	3rd			

Hungry horses

The pie chart shows the percentages of different foods the ponies eat each day. Look at the examples to see how to add and subtract percentages. Then answer the questions on the ponies' menu.

This is how you add and subtract percentages:

$$\begin{array}{r} 20.5\% \\ +15.3\% \\ \hline 35.8\% \end{array} \qquad \begin{array}{r} 16.7\% \\ -\ 4.2\% \\ \hline 12.5\% \end{array}$$

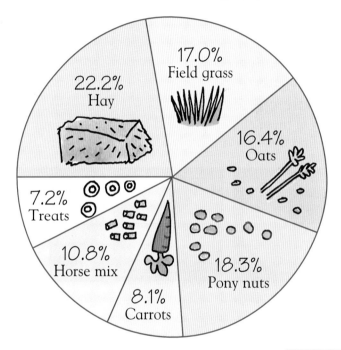

22.2%
Hay

17.0%
Field grass

16.4%
Oats

7.2%
Treats

10.8%
Horse mix

18.3%
Pony nuts

8.1%
Carrots

What percentage of the ponies' food is hay?

What percentage of the ponies' food is field grass and oats together?

The ponies eat less horse mix than pony nuts. How much less?

What should all the percentages in the pie chart add up to?

Does the pie chart have the correct sum total? Use a calculator to check.

yes	no

Fractions

The shapes and patterns in these mosaics will help you work on fractions. Study the examples below to find out what is meant by a fraction, then try to solve the puzzles.

Fractions

When a thing, or a group of things, or a number is divided into equal parts, each part is called a fraction.

Whole mosaic piece

Half a piece

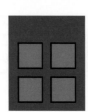

A whole bag of 4 pieces

Half a bag of 2 pieces

6 Six

3 Three is half of six

One-half is written

$\frac{1}{2}$

This number is called the numerator

This number is called the denominator

Mosaic circles

Each of these circles is divided into a different number of sections. For each one find a sticker answer to show what fraction the section represents.

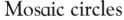

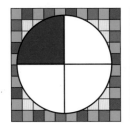

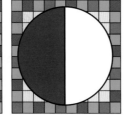

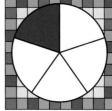

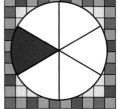

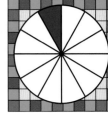

Colour the fraction

Colour in the correct number of sections in the circles to represent the fractions on the right.

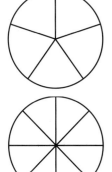

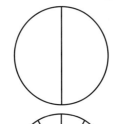

$\frac{2}{5}$

$\frac{1}{2}$

$\frac{3}{8}$

$\frac{7}{12}$

Panel colours

There are 9 squares in this mosaic panel. What fraction of the whole panel are the different coloured squares? Find the sticker answers.

Equivalent fractions

When 2 different fractions equal the same amount they are called equivalent fractions, e.g. $\frac{1}{2}$ is the same as $\frac{2}{4}$ and $\frac{3}{6}$

$$\frac{1}{2} \qquad \frac{2}{4} \qquad \frac{3}{6}$$

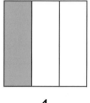 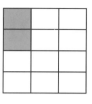

$$\frac{1}{3} \qquad \frac{2}{8} \qquad \frac{2}{12}$$

$$\frac{1}{4} \qquad \frac{1}{6} \qquad \frac{3}{9}$$

Mosaic match

Study the mosaic squares. Which ones are the same amount? Draw a line to match them up and discover the equivalent fractions.

Adding and subtracting fractions

To add or subtract fractions, first check that the fractions have the same denominator, then add or subtract the numerators.

$$\frac{1}{4} \;+\; \frac{2}{4} \;=\; \frac{3}{4}$$

Numerator

Denominator

Add the fraction

Solve these fraction additions and fill in the boxes with the correct answers.

$$\frac{2}{5} \;+\; \frac{1}{5} \;=\; \boxed{}$$

$$\frac{2}{6} \;+\; \frac{1}{6} \;=\; \boxed{}$$

$$\frac{4}{12} \;+\; \frac{1}{12} \;=\; \boxed{}$$

$$\frac{3}{8} \;+\; \frac{2}{8} \;=\; \boxed{}$$

Fraction subtraction

Find the correct sticker answers to these fraction subtractions.

$$\frac{2}{3} \;-\; \frac{1}{3} \;=\; \stackrel{\star}{}$$

$$\frac{3}{4} \;-\; \frac{1}{4} \;=\; \stackrel{\star}{}$$

$$\frac{5}{6} \;-\; \frac{2}{6} \;=\; \stackrel{\star}{}$$

$$\frac{7}{10} \;-\; \frac{3}{10} \;=\; \stackrel{\star}{}$$

13

Lions and tigers

You will need
- Two players
- Thin card
- Scissors
- 16 lion and tiger counter stickers from the sticker sheet
- Answer card from the sticker sheet
- Scrap paper and pencil to work out the sums

Making the cards
- Stick the counter stickers and answer card on to thin card.
- Cut round the stickers to make 8 lion counters, 8 tiger counters, and an answer card.

Aim
- The aim of the game is to get three of your counters on to the squares in your opponent's den and remove as many of his/her counters from the board as possible.

Playing the game
- Choose either lion or tiger counters. Tigers go first.

- Set the counters out in two rows on opposite sides of the board in the marked spaces.

- Playing on the white squares only, take it in turns to move one of your counters forwards one square. You must move diagonally to the right or left and on to an empty square. You cannot move backwards.

- Before you move your counter on to a square you must solve the calculation shown on that square.

- If you cannot solve the calculation, you miss a go.

- If your opponent's counter is on a square diagonally next to your counter, but the square beyond is free, you may jump on to the free square and remove your opponent's counter from the board.

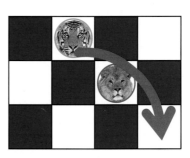

- The winner is the first player to get three counters on to the squares in their opponent's den.

61 + 64

7 x 7

40 + 2

4 x 3

Den

9 − 125   59 − 36   82 − 57   65 − 33

71 + 29   326 + 412   83 + 22

3 ÷ 2   32 ÷ 4   60 ÷ 12   84 ÷ 12

8 x 5   3 x 3   7 x 4

6 − 7   22 − 5   38 − 24   170 − 65

33 + 55   16 + 14   59 + 7

1 ÷ 3   54 ÷ 9   45 ÷ 5   88 ÷ 8

6 x 8   9 x 2   12 x 12

Answers

Pages 2/3 Fun and games

Badminton colours
The numbers that can be divided by 2 are: **16 450
76 80 108 30 100 102 50 700 500 60**
The numbers that can be divided by 5 are:
450 80 30 100 50 700 35 365 500 60
The numbers that can be divided by 10 are:
450 80 30 100 50 700 500 60

Batty additions
14 = 7 + 7
56 = 39 + 9 + 8
111 = 59 + 41 + 10 + 1
375 = 205 + 88 + 70 + 12

Singles and doubles
14 people can play singles tennis: 7 x 2 = 14
16 people can play singles badminton: 8 x 2 = 16
24 people can play doubles table tennis: 6 x 4 = 24
28 people can play doubles tennis: 7 x 4 = 28

Net numbers

¹1	6		²3	3
9		³6	5	
	⁴5		⁵2	⁶1
⁷1	8			9
4		⁸1	5	6

Court calculations
320 ÷ 16 = 20 − 10 = 10 + (3 x 8) = 34 − 17 =
17 − 9 = 8 x (12 x 5) = 480 − 282 = 198 ÷ 11 =
18 − 3 = 15 ÷ 3 = 5

Pages 4/5 Number patterns

Footprints in the sand
1 4 9 **16** 25 36 49 64 81 100 121 144

Camp fire
The odd numbers are: 1 3 11 51 77
The even numbers are: 6 14 20 38 46

Bear tracks
1 + 3 = 4
1 + 3 + 5 = 9
1 + 3 + 5 + 7 = 16
1 + 3 + 5 + 7 + 9 = 25
The pattern continues.

Consecutive numbers
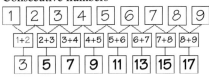

The numbers in the pattern are odd numbers.

Torch light
2 3 5 7 11 13 17 19

Prime number trail
19 23 29 31 37 41

Pages 6/7 2-D and 3-D shapes

2-D descriptions

Pentagon
5 sides

Rectangle
2 pairs of sides the same

Triangle
3 sides

Square
4 sides the same

Hexagon
6 sides

2-D symmetry
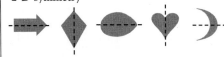

Faces, corners, and edges

	Faces	Corners	Edges
Pyramid	5	5	8
Cube	6	8	12
Triangular prism	5	6	9
Hexagonal prism	8	12	18

Polyhedra
There are **4** polyhedra. They are the **pyramid,
cube, prism,** and **cuboid.**
The regular polyhedra are the **cube, tetrahedron,**
and **octahedron.**
The **pyramid** is **NOT** a regular polyhedron.

Page 8 Averages

Busy line
The mean call time is **6 minutes**: 54 ÷ 9 = 6
The mode call time is **4 minutes**: There are 3 calls
of **4 minutes.**
The median call time is **5 minutes**:
3 4 4 4 ⑤ 5 6 9 14

TV competition
The mean number of calls is **600**:
4200 ÷ 7 = **600**
The mode number of calls is **500**: 2 operators
receive **500 calls.**
The median number of calls is **500**:
100 200 500 ⑤⓪⓪ 600 700 1600

Page 9 Timing
Day 1   Go by train ➜ Visit the seaside ➜ Eat an
ice-cream ➜ Buy souvenirs in the market
Day 2   Go by bike ➜ Visit a wildlife park ➜ Make
a phone call ➜ Go skating
Day 3   Go by bus ➜ Climb a mountain ➜ Have a
picnic ➜ Visit a funfair

Pages 10/11 Charts and graphs

Pony rides
Lucy was chosen **18** times.
Monty was chosen **32** times.
Star was chosen **24** times.
Monty had the most rides.
Lucy had fewer than **20** rides.
There were **94** rides in total.

Saddle chart
Amber   8 8 4   8 + 8 + 4 = 20
Lucy   8 8 2   8 + 8 + 2 = 18
Monty   8 8 8 8   8 + 8 + 8 + 8 = 32
Star   8 8 8   8 + 8 + 8 = 24

Monty wins
Monty has won **23** rosettes.
Monty has come first **5** times.
The difference is **2.**

Block graph

Hungry horses
22.2% of the ponies' food is hay.
33.4% of the ponies' food is field grass and oats:
17.0% + 16.4% = 33.4 %
The ponies eat **7.5%** less horse mix than pony nuts:
18.3% − 10.8% = 7.5%
Percent means out of **100.** All the percentages
should add up to **100.**
Yes, the pie chart does have the correct sum total.

Pages 12/13 Fractions

Mosaic circles
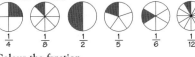

Colour the fraction
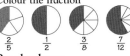

Panel colours
Red $\frac{1}{9}$ Purple $\frac{3}{9}$ Green $\frac{1}{9}$ Yellow $\frac{4}{9}$

Mosaic match
$\frac{1}{3}$ is the same as $\frac{3}{9}$ $\frac{2}{8}$ is the same as $\frac{1}{4}$
$\frac{2}{12}$ is the same as $\frac{1}{6}$

Add the fraction
$\frac{2}{5} + \frac{1}{5} = \frac{3}{5}$
$\frac{2}{6} + \frac{1}{6} = \frac{3}{6}$
$\frac{4}{12} + \frac{1}{12} = \frac{5}{12}$
$\frac{3}{8} + \frac{2}{8} = \frac{5}{8}$

Fraction subtraction
$\frac{2}{3} - \frac{1}{3} = \frac{1}{3}$
$\frac{3}{4} - \frac{1}{4} = \frac{2}{4}$
$\frac{5}{6} - \frac{2}{6} = \frac{3}{6}$
$\frac{7}{10} - \frac{3}{10} = \frac{4}{10}$

A DORLING KINDERSLEY BOOK

Editor Rachel Harrison
Senior Designer Jane Horne
Managing Editor Sarah Phillips
Managing Art Editor Peter Bailey
Jacket Design Mark Haygarth
Production Ruth Cobb
Illustrations by Tim Hutchinson
Photography by Peter Chadwick, Dave King, Bob Langrish,
Susanna Price, Tim Ridley, Clive Streeter
Lion pages 4 and 5 and sticker page © Jerry Young

Picture credits: p.10 'Wychwood Dynascha' Mrs G Harwood, 'Parlington Pepsi' and 'Parlingoton Dainty
Maid' Mrs G D Johnson, 'Spinway Bright Morning" Miss S Hodgekins,
'Brutt' Tobert Oliver

First published in Great Britain in 1997 by Dorling Kindersley Ltd,
80 Strand, London WC2R 0RL

Copyright © 1998 Dorling Kindersley Limited, London

Visit us on the World Wide Web at http://www.dk.com

All rights reserved. No part of this publication may be reproduced, stored in a retrieval
system, or transmitted in any form, or by any means electronic, mechanical, photocopying,
recording, or otherwise, without the prior written permission of the copyright owner.

A CIP catalogue record for this book is available from the British Library.

ISBN   978-0-7513-5680-9

Colour reproduction by Colourscan, Singapore

Printed and bound by Thumbprints in Malaysia